NEW FOREST

Halswood

Published by Halswood Stationers

British Library Cataloguing-in-Publication Data
A CIP record for this title is available
from the British Library

ISBN 978 0 85717 004 0

HALSWOOD STATIONERS

Halsgrove House,
Ryelands Industrial Estate,
Bagley Road, Wellington, Somerset TA21 9PZ
Tel: 01823 653777   Fax: 01823 216796
email: sales@halsgrove.com

Part of the Halsgrove group of companies
Information on all Halsgrove titles is available at:
www.halsgrove.com

Printed and bound in China by
Toppan Leefung Printing Ltd (010)

Front cover: Ponies stand beside the Ober Water
stream close to Ober Corner.

Back cover: As we head towards autumn, the
heather has just about finished blooming and the
bracken has begun to take on a golden glow in
this gloriously lit sunrise.

Title page: Ridges of heathland are bisected by
trees in lower lying areas of Soarley Bottom.

Right: Mark Ash Wood.

Overleaf: Larch trees grow tall and straight in
plantations such as here in Puckpits Inclosure.

YOUR ADDRESS BOOK

The New Forest National Park was created in 2005 and is one of England's newest as well as smallest national parks at 57,000 ha. Famous for its Open Forest, where Forest animals – especially the famous New Forest ponies and red deer – are free to roam, there is also a coast, the Avon Valley and an ancient landscape of field and woods. Within striking distance lie large urban conurbations, yet the Forest is an oasis of peace and calm. Although the Open Forest is the most complete heathland in Britain, with an exceptional wildlife, the landscape and its wildlife are the result of hundreds of years of management by man, a living tradition that continues today.

Chasing the light across this precious landscape can be very rewarding, but it also poses a considerable challenge. You can be sitting waiting for the sun to rise, only to find a bank of cloud rolling in from the east blocking out the magical dawn light. Or sheltering waiting for heavy rain to pass over and leave storm clouds and dramatic light. The best photographic conditions are often around dawn and dusk, when the light can be a revelation, transforming a mundane landscape into something quite sublime. Patience to simply sit and wait for the ideal moment is essential – and that is what master photographer Mike Read demonstrates again and again in the collection of superb images reproduced here.

Address books tend to be well used and have a long life. Along with important contact details, they keep track of the user's friends and acquaintances, tracing their lives over time and from place to place. And, if properly attended to, an address book eventually becomes a journal in itself, and an attractive and permanent keepsake. Whether bought as a gift or for personal use, this New Forest Address Book, with its superb pictorial reminders of the national park, will provide years of pleasure.

USEFUL ADDRESSES AND TELEPHONE NUMBERS

A

Low mist seems to be heralding the end of summer and greeting the beginning of autumn, a fabulous season of plenty in the Forest as trees, shrubs and flowering plants all produce seeds or fruit that birds and mammals can feed on.

A

The Solent and other parts of the New Forest coast form an important area for migrant, wintering and breeding birds. Here, as the sun rises over the Isle of Wight, Brent geese can be seen beside feeding ducks and waders.

B

As we head deep into autumn and towards the short days
of winter, grass grows less well, so many ponies will be
found in the woods where other foods are perhaps available.

B

B

B

Ancient beech in autumn.

C

A spider's web in autumnal beech branches is enhanced with droplets of moisture deposited during a misty night.

C

C

C

The colour of the sky deepens as the sun disappears over the distant horizon and mist begins to form in the valley below Picket Post.

D

New Forest pony, Hincheslea Moor.

D

D

D

As the sun rises over a group of maturing Scots pines, its rays
penetrate the light mist and soon the frost will be gone.

E

A mare and her young foal wander the heath of Ragged Boys Hill.

E

E

E

Oaks reflected in a New Forest stream. Spring, as shown
here, is a superb time to visit an oak wood when many birds
will be singing. In autumn, deer will feed on fallen acorns.

F

A frosted fond.

F

F

F

This foal may still suckle occasionally when its mother allows but it is now mostly reliant on grazing and browsing for its nutrition.

G

The late Sir Dudley Forwood, the Official Verderer for eight years,
is remembered close to his former Burley Old House home.
The two oak trees were planted in Sir Dudley's memory.

G

G

G

Often referred to as 'Lady of the Woods', silver birches add grace to a scene even when they grow on open heathland such as here at Ober Heath.

H

A pony shelters from a cooling breeze in the lee
of a group of snow-covered gorse bushes.

H

H

H

The sun has risen quite high and a little mist remains to help cast beams of light through the branches of this magnificent pollarded beech.

Well into November, fallow bucks may still associate with groups of does in case one comes into season but most will be mated during the rut in October.

I

These bluebells are in Broomy Inclosure.

J

Pony at sunrise.

J

To wander among some of the Forest's ancient beech trees has
been compared to entering a magnificent cathedral. Certainly
standing beside some of these wonderful trees and speculating
what history they have witnessed can be rather humbling.

K

As we head towards autumn, the heather has just
about finished blooming and the bracken has begun
to take on a golden glow in this gloriously lit sunrise.

K

The Blackwater Arboretum off the Rhinefield Ornamental
Drive holds a wide range of tree species from around the
world. In autumn the colours can be quite spectacular.

L

L

L

With global warming now a recognised reality, more frequent
storms cause scenes like this to become increasingly common.

M

Ponies stand beside the Ober Water
stream close to Ober Corner.

M

M

M

Beeches in winter. Though this may look like an autumn
photograph, it was actually taken in December.

Light rays break through a stand of Scots pines and bring life
to the scene. Purple moor grass shows that the foreground
soil is permanently wet so beware where you walk!

N

Blue sky and sunshine herald a thaw after this springtime
snowfall. This scene was taken from the car park at
Mogshade Hill towards Bratley Inclosure and Bratley Wood.

O

O

Foals follow their mother's example and, as soon
as they can, they will walk, trot or even gallop to keep up.

O

Oaks and distant Scots pines are silhouetted
against a glorious, clear-sky sunset.

Autumn colours at their best beside the Linwood Road at Moyles Court.

PQ

Sun peers round an aged beech tree to herald another spring day in the New Forest.

R

The location may be called Hincheslea 'Moor' but this is true heathland, a rare habitat often full of endangered wildlife.

R

Tranquil woodlands.

A well grown foal still sticks close to its mother
as the photographer appears out of the autumnal mist!

S

S

S

Timber lies stacked beside a Forest road awaiting collection in Roe Inclosure. While we like to think of this National Park purely as a recreational and conservation area, it has to be remembered that this is a working forest.

Scots pines stand silhouetted against a deeply-coloured sunset. Soon the light will fade and another memorable day in the New Forest will pass and the night shift, such as owls and badgers, will emerge to begin their activities.

T

A couple of fallow deer bucks seen on a roadside.
In autumn, male deer wander widely in search of
mates so it is the best season to encounter them.

UV

Evening skies over Hatchet Pond.

Evening sunlight picks out the blooming heather while the
trees of Soarley Beeches add a typical New Forest backdrop.

W

Sunlight penetrates the mist of a late autumn morning in the oak plantation in Broomy Inclosure.